REMOVED FROM THE INVENTORY
OF THE TAMPA-HILLSBOROUGH
COUNTY PUBLIC LIBRARY SYSTEM

W9-AQL-311

FOLLOW

TAMPA PUBLIC LIBRARY

THE SUNSET

by Herman and Nina Schneider

Pictures by Lucille Corcos

494690

Doubleday & Company, Inc.
Garden City, New York

For our children
on whom the sun rises and sets

Copyright, 1952 by Herman & Nina Schneider
All rights reserved
Library of Congress No. 52-6370
Lithographed in the U. S. A.

EVERY EVENING

the sun sets. The day ends,

and darkness covers your house

and all the other houses in your town.

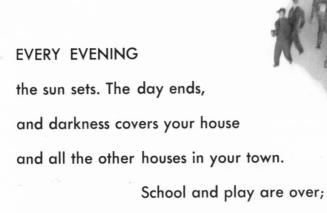

School and play are over;

fathers hurry home from work.

Mothers tuck their babies into bed

as night comes.

After the dark of night

there is always the fresh, new day.

Every morning, when you wake up,

there is daylight outside your window.

3

What makes the new day come after the night?

And what makes the night follow the day?

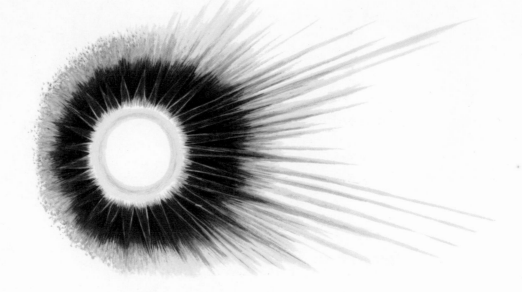

The light of the sun brings the day.

It is day time for you

when your part of the earth is in the sunlight.

The setting of the sun brings the night.

It is night time for you

when your part of the earth

is out of the sunlight.

Night is the time of no sunlight.

Day and night follow each other

because the earth keeps turning all the time.

4

The earth is a huge ball

that turns through the sunlight and darkness.

Into the sunlight and daytime,

into the darkness and night time,

the earth keeps turning steadily.

What happens in other lands,

in faraway farms and cities?

When night time comes to you,

does it also come to other people in other lands?

Let's follow the sunset and see.

It is sunset over the land near the Atlantic Ocean.

Day is ending in the big cities and in the little

towns and farms of the Eastern Coast

of the United States.

The fathers leave their offices and factories.
In cars and busses, in subway trains and
trolleys, they head for home.

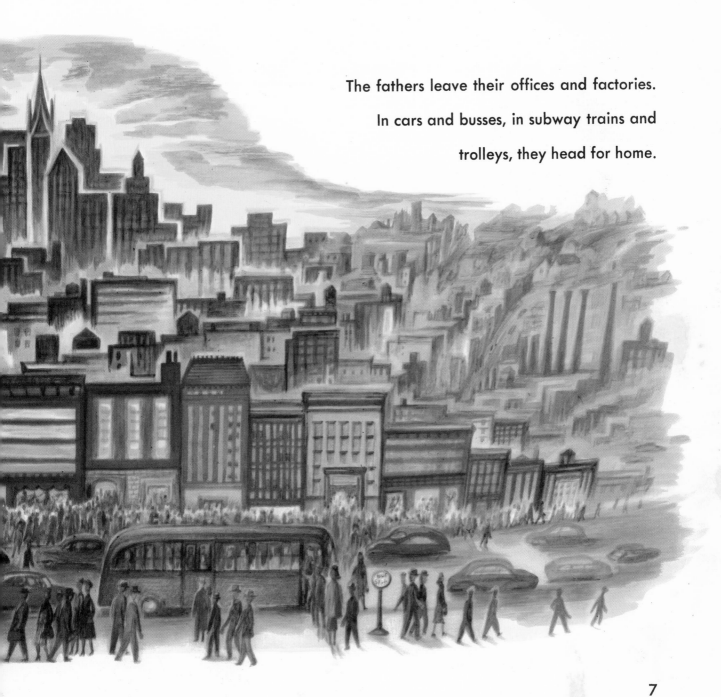

At home, food is sizzling on the stove.

Children are putting away

books and skates and bats.

The babies are drowsy

in their cribs

as their mothers

sing them to sleep.

Sleep, Ba - a - by, sleep. Thy fa - ther wat - ches the

sheep. Thy mo - ther is shak - ing the dream - land tree and

down falls a lit - tle dream on thee. Sleep, Ba - by, sleep.

Soon it is dark night over the big
cities and little towns, over the
farms and beaches all along this
part of the earth.

But westward beyond the mountains,

the sunset has just begun.

9

Twilight is settling over
the Central Plains of
the land, over dark
northern forests,
over great fields
of wheat and corn.

In Mexico, too,
the night is coming on.

Here, on a dirt road,

a family is riding home from a fiesta

in a wagon drawn by slow oxen.

The air smells of lime trees.

An Indian woman walks by,

carrying a basket of beans on her head.

A burro calls

to another burro

in the field.

The children in the wagon are tired,

and their mother sings them a song.

Sleep, oh sleep, my chil-dren. Go to sleep.

Night is time for sleep-ing. Sleep, oh sleep.

Now it is dark night in Mexico

and in all the part of the earth that has

circled away from the sunlight.

The children are asleep in the starry dark.

But farther westward, sunset is just beginning.

In the land of the cowboy
and his cattle, it is sunset.

14

The bright paintbox colors fade out of the sky.

Over the Rocky Mountains, the sun sinks out of sight.

Darkness, like a soft velvet ribbon, rolls over the prairies and over the cowboys who are singing the cattle to rest with a song.

Oh slow up, do-gies, stop your ro-vin' 'round You've wan-dered and

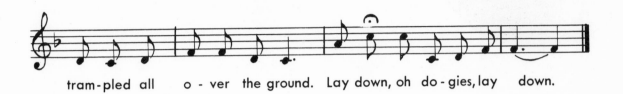

tram-pled all o-ver the ground. Lay down, oh do-gies, lay down.

Now the cattle are quiet

and the children in the ranch houses

are fast asleep.

It is night time over the prairies

and along the Western shore.

But over the Pacific Ocean

the twilight is just beginning.

17

Now the next part of the earth and sea

is moving from light into night.

Over Hawaii and the many little Pacific

islands, the clouds are colored with

the last rays of the setting sun.

The fluttering fish nets are still,

and the pink sails are folded

away from the wind.

18

The boys are digging a fire pit

for a picnic supper.

Along the darkening beach the fisher fathers

can hear the mothers singing the children to sleep.

A - bove is the sky. Be - low is the sea.

And here is my boat, just wait - ing for me.

Now it is night time

for the fishes in the sea

and for the island fishermen

and their families.

Starlight and firelight

shine upon them.

But far away,

on the other shore of the Pacific Ocean

daylight is just ending.

494690

Turning, turning,
the earth keeps turning away
from the west and the sunlight. And now
evening time is coming to the Asian
land, to the Indian Ocean and
the China Sea.

The fathers come home from the rice fields
and teak forests, from sampans and silk shops.

The children are catching fireflies

to put into lanterns.

The firefly lanterns will give light in the dark night.

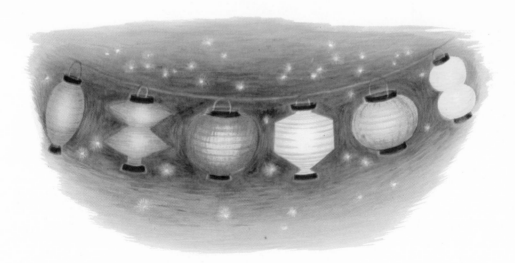

The sleepy small children

try to watch the flickering fireflies,

but their eyes close while Mother

sings a song and Brother

plays a flute.

Fire - fly   lul - la - by   on   a bam-boo flute.   Lul - la - by   for

Ba - by.   Small   lu   lu   lu   lu   lu,   lu   lu - u   lu.

Now everything is quiet along the
Yangtze River in China. Dark
night has settled softly over the
Asian land and sea, over Australia and
the islands of the Pacific.

But westward, in other lands,
the children are just beginning to feel drowsy.

The sunset and the dark

come steadily across the earth bringing

night to each place in turn.

Twilight covers the Red Sea

and the hills of Turkey.

It is getting too dark

to work any longer

in the orange groves of Israel.

The orange pickers return to

the buildings where

many families

live.

The children are carrying blankets to the big outdoor

fireplace. Tonight there will be a party outdoors, and they

will fall asleep to the sound of gay dance music.

Ho, ho, ho, ho, ho, ha, ho, ha, ha,   ha, ha, ha, ho, ha,   let's have a

par - ty. We'll all dance the ho - ra. Ga-ther round the ta - ble. we'll

give you a treat — spin - ning tops to play with, sweet-meats to eat.

It is bright,

starry night in Israel.

But farther west,

where the earth is turning away from the

sunlight, evening has just begun.

In the hill country
of Africa,
a drowsy baby
listens to her sister
singing.

30

Lu - la, Ba - by, la, la. Close your eyes.

Lu - la, Ba - by, la, la, vel - vet eyes.

In the field below,

their father and mother are still at work

in the deepening twilight.

When it is too dark to work any longer,

they will come home

with a jug of water from the river

and a basket of yams

from the garden.

It is night

on the hills and

plains of Africa and

all along this vast part

of the earth.

But westward

the day is just leaving the land.

Fathers and brothers come home
from the olive groves and vineyards
in Spain and France,
from mountain pastures and valley fields.

In old towns and freshly planted fields,

people see the sun setting as they return

to their homes.

In a house near
the shore of England a
mother is thinking of her sailor
husband as she sings a song to her baby.

1 { Sleep, My child, and peace at - tend thee all
    Guard - ian an - gels God will send thee all

I, my love, am vi - gil keep - ing all

1 { through the night.
    through the night.
    Soft the drow - sy hours are

through the night.

creep - ing, hill and vale in slum - ber steep - ing.

All this part of the world

turns smoothly from daylight into dark.

The quiet night will cover the islands of England and

the lands of Europe. Stars will shine over

flowering fields and shining beaches.

On the deck of a great ocean liner,

the sailors and passengers are watching

the first pale stars appear in the sky.

They think of their families and friends

as they whistle and sing an old sea song.

Oh, Shen - an - doah, I long to hear you. A - way, you rol - ling

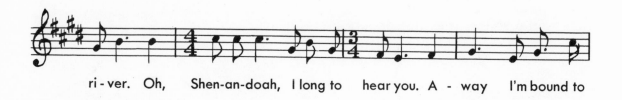

ri - ver. Oh, Shen - an - doah, I long to hear you. A - way I'm bound to

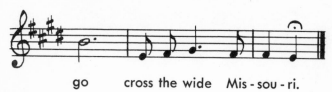

go cross the wide Mis - sou - ri.

Now it is night
over the Atlantic Ocean,
and this part of the earth
will turn steadily
through the dark
until it turns once again
through the sunrise.

41

Now the earth

has turned all the way around.

As it turned,

darkness rolled westward

over mountains and prairies,

over islands and oceans.

The darkness fell softly

over farmers and fishermen,

over mothers and children.

The turning of the earth

brought dark starry night,

then pink dawn and bright day.

Now once again

the sun is setting along the land

near the Atlantic Ocean.

Once again this part of the earth

is circling into darkness.

From sunset to sunset, one day has passed.

The names Herman and Nina Schneider immediately call
to mind interesting and accurate books in science.
Together they have written thirty-three books for children.
Many of these books are best sellers in the United States and
they have been translated into twenty-eight foreign languages
for use in other countries.

Both Mr. and Mrs. Schneider were born in Europe but
they went to schools in this country.
They presently live in New York City.
Herman Schneider has been a teacher of students in
elementary school, junior and senior high school as well as
in college, graduate school and schools of education.
He was also the Science Supervisor of
all of the elementary schools of New York City.

Lucille Corcos, the illustrator, is a native New Yorker and
a foremost artist in the Fine Arts and commercial fields today.
Her work has been shown at
the Metropolitan Museum and in museums abroad.
She has done covers for such magazines as
Vogue, Fortune, Life, Holiday, Harper's and *Harper's Bazaar.*
She has illustrated several distinguished books and
painted a series of murals for
the Waldorf Astoria Hotel in New York City.

Lithographed in the U.S.A. by Columbia Lithographic Co., Inc., N. Y. C.

REMOVED FROM THE INVENTORY
OF THE TAMPA-HILLSBOROUGH
COUNTY PUBLIC LIBRARY SYSTEM

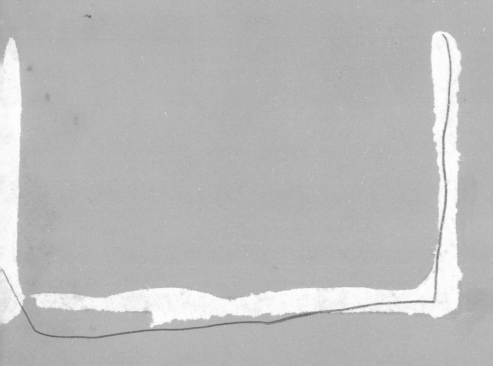